SMASH HITS
boy band ballads
14 GREAT SONGS

This publication is not authorised for sale in the United States of America and / or Canada

WISE PUBLICATIONS
part of The Music Sales Group
London / New York / Paris / Sydney / Copenhagen / Berlin / Madrid / Tokyo

Published by
WISE PUBLICATIONS
8/9 Frith Street, London, W1D 3JB, England.

Exclusive distributors:
MUSIC SALES LIMITED
Distribution Centre, Newmarket Road,
Bury St Edmunds, Suffolk, IP33 3YB, England.

MUSIC SALES PTY LIMITED
120 Rothschild Avenue, Rosebery, NSW 2018, Australia.

Order No. AM984907
ISBN ISBN 1-84609-431-3

Cover designed by Fresh Lemon.
Cover photography courtesy of LFI.
Printed in the EU.

www.musicsales.com

All About You

Words & Music by Thomas Fletcher

C
Am
Dm
G
It's all a - bout you,
it's all a - bout you.
C
E7
Am
Yes - ter-day you asked me some-thing I thought you knew.
So I
F
G
C
G
told you with a smile...
It's all a - bout you.
C
E7
Am
Then you whis-pered in my ear and you told me too,
2° Instrumental till *

F
G7
said you'd make my life worth - while,
it's all a - bout
C
C7
F
you.
And
I would an - swer
*
Fm
C
G/B
Am
all your wish - es
if you asked me to.
But if
D7
G
Gaug
you de - ny me
one of your kiss - es,
don't know what I'd
do.

C
E7
Am
3
So hold me close and say three words like you used to do.
Am/G
F
1.
G
Danc - ing on the kit - chen tiles, it's all a - bout
C
G
2.
G
you. Yeah.
yes, you
F
G
F
made my life worth while.
So I told you with this

Fm6
N.C.
C
smile… It's all a - bout you.
It's all a -
Am
Dm
G
- bout you, it's all a - bout you ba - by.
C
Am
Dm
1.
G
It's all a - bout you, it's all a - bout you ba - by.
2.
Fm6
N.C.
Free time
C6/9
- bout you. It's all a - bout you.

All I Have To Give

Words & Music by Full Force

C♭maj7
B♭sus2
B♭m7
G♭
A♭
fr4
walk a thou - sand miles.
I don't care
if he buys
B♭m
G♭
A♭
Fm
G♭sus2
you nice things does his gifts come from the heart?
I don't know.
G♭
A♭
C♭maj7
B♭m7
But if you were my girl,
I'd make it so we'd
F7sus4
F7
B♭m
ne - ver be a - part.
But my love is all

G♭ A♭ B♭m G♭ A♭
fr4 fr4
I have to give. With - out you I don't think I could live.
Fm7 G♭maj7 G♭ A♭ A♭/C D♭
fr4 fr4
I wish I could give the world to you but love is all I
1. 2.
C♭maj7 A♭sus4 C♭maj7 A♭sus4
fr4 fr4
have to give. 2. When you talk have to give to you.
B♭m A♭/C D♭ G♭6 A♭/C D♭
Hey girl, I don't want you to cry no more in - side

G♭maj9
fr3
A♭
fr4
B♭m
A♭/C
D♭
G♭6
All the mon - ey in the world could ne - ver
A♭/C
D♭
C♭maj7
B♭11
B♭m7
add up to all the love I have in - side. I love you
N.C.
ba - by. And I will give it to you,
all I can give, all I can give. All, ev-'ry-thing I have is for you.

G♭
A♭
fr4
You, you, you, you, you, you, you, you, what I need. My love is
A♭/C
D♭
C♭maj7
A♭sus4
fr4
all that I have to give. My love is all
G♭
B♭m
G♭
A♭
fr4
I have to give with - out you I don't think I can live
Fm7
G♭maj7
fr4
G♭
A♭
fr4
A♭/C
D♭
I wish I could give the world to you, but love is all I

C♭maj7
A♭sus4
fr4
N.C.
have to give. But my love is all I have to give
with - out you I don't think I can live, I wish I could give
C♭maj7
the world to you but love is all I have to give
A♭sus4
fr4
G♭
A♭
fr4
B♭m7
to you. All

Verse 2:
When you talk does it seem like he's not
Even listening to a word you say?
That's okay babe, just tell me your problems
I'll try my best to kiss them all away
Does he leave when you need him the most?
Does his friends get all your time?
Baby please – I'm on my knees
Praying for the day that you'll be mine

But my love is all I have to give *etc.*

Best In Me

Words & Music by Bill Padley & Jem Godfrey

Bm7
E7
F
Gadd9
ev - er wan - na lose this feel - ing, I don't wan - na spend a mo - ment a - part. 'Cause
Cadd9
E7
Am
Am7/G
D7/F♯
you bring out the best in me, like no - one else can do. That's why I'm by
Dm7
To Coda
G11
G
1.
Csus2
Am add11
your side and that's why I love you.
2.
Cadd9
C
E7
(Vocal ad lib.)
you. (Ooh, ooh, ooh, ooh, ooh.)

Am
Am7/G
D7/F♯
Dm7
G
D.𝄋. al Coda
(Ooh.)
(Ooh,
ah.)
And you
Coda
G
Dadd9
2fr
F♯7
'Cause you bring out the best in me, like
Bm
Bm7/A
E7/G♯
Em7
no - one else can do.
That's why I'm by your side
A11
4fr
A
D
(Love you.)
(Love you.)
and that's why I love you, love you.
'Cause

Verse 2:
Every day that I'm here with you
I know that it feels right (so right)
I just gotta be near you
Every day and every night (every night)
And you know that we belong together
It just had to be you and me.

'Cause you bring out the best in me *etc.*

Father And Son

Words & Music by Cat Stevens

G
D
C
Am
settle down; if you want to, you can marry. Look at me:
G
Em
To Coda
Am
D
G
D
I am old, but I'm happy. I was once like you are now, and I know
C
Am
G
Em
that it's not easy to be calm when you've found something go-
Am
D
G
D
-ing on. But take your time, think a lot; think of ev-

C
Am
G
Em
D
-'ry-thing_ you've got._ For you_ will
still be here_ to-mor-row,_ but your dreams_ may_
G
C/G
G
C/G
G
Bm
not.
How can I_ try to ex-plain?_ When I do_
(2° instrumental)
Cadd9
Am
G
Em
_ he turns_ a-way a-gain._ It's al - ways_ been the same,_ same old_
Am
D
G
Bm
_ sto - ry._ From the mo - ment I_ could talk,_ I was or-

Cadd9
Am
G
Em
- dered to lis - ten. Now there's a way and I know that I
D
G
D
C
1.
G
C/G
have to go a - way. I know I have to go.
G
C/G
2.
G
C/E
D.S. al Coda
G
C/G
C/E
It's not
Coda
Am
D
G
Bm
- py. All the times that I've cried, keep - ing all

Cadd9
Am
G
Em
the things I knew inside: it's hard, but it's harder to ignore
Am
D
G
Bm
it. If they were right, I'd agree; but it's them
Cadd9
Am
G
Em
they know, not me. Now there's a way, and I know that I
D
G
D
C
G
have to go away. I know I have to go.

Guilty

Words & Music by Gary Barlow, Eliot Kennedy,
Tim Woodcock & Duncan James

F♯
Bsus2
I nev - er want to hear the things they got - ta say.
Don't try to tell me how he treats you is - n't bad.
F♯
Bsus2
Esus2
2fr
I've found ev - 'ry - thing I need.
I need you back in my life.
I nev - er want - ed a - ny
I nev - er want - ed just to
G♯m9
4fr
Esus2
2fr
more than I could see.
be the oth - er guy.
I on - ly want you to be -
I nev - er want to live a
G♯m9
4fr
F♯
- lieve.
lie.
If it's wrong to tell the truth what am

Bsus2
F♯
I sup - posed to do when all I wan - na do is speak my
Bsus2
F♯
mind? If it's wrong to do what's right I'm pre - pared
Bsus2
Eadd9
B
to tes - ti - fy, if lov - in' you with all my heart's a crime,
G♯m7(add11)
To Coda
1.
F♯
then I'm guil - ty.

2.
F♯
G♯m7
4fr
B
guil - ty.
Girl, I fol - low my heart,
fol - low the truth,
F♯
D♯m9
4fr
G♯dim
4fr
G♯m7
4fr
right from the start.
He led me to you,
please don't leave me this way,
Badd9
C♯sus4
4fr
C♯
4fr
D.S. al Coda
I'm guil - ty, now all
I have
to say…
If it's
Coda
F♯
Bsus2
F♯
guil - ty.
What am
I sup - posed to do?
And I'm
guil - ty.

Bsus2
F♯
Bsus2
Guil - ty. And I'm guil - ty. I'm pre - pared to tes - ti - fy. If it's
Eadd9
B
G♯m7(add11)
wrong to do what's right then tell me a - bout this feel - ing in - side.
F♯
Bsus2
3
Eadd9
B
If lov - in' you with all my heart's a crime,
G♯m7(add11)
F♯
I'm guil - ty.

I Swear

Words & Music by Frank Myers & Gary Baker

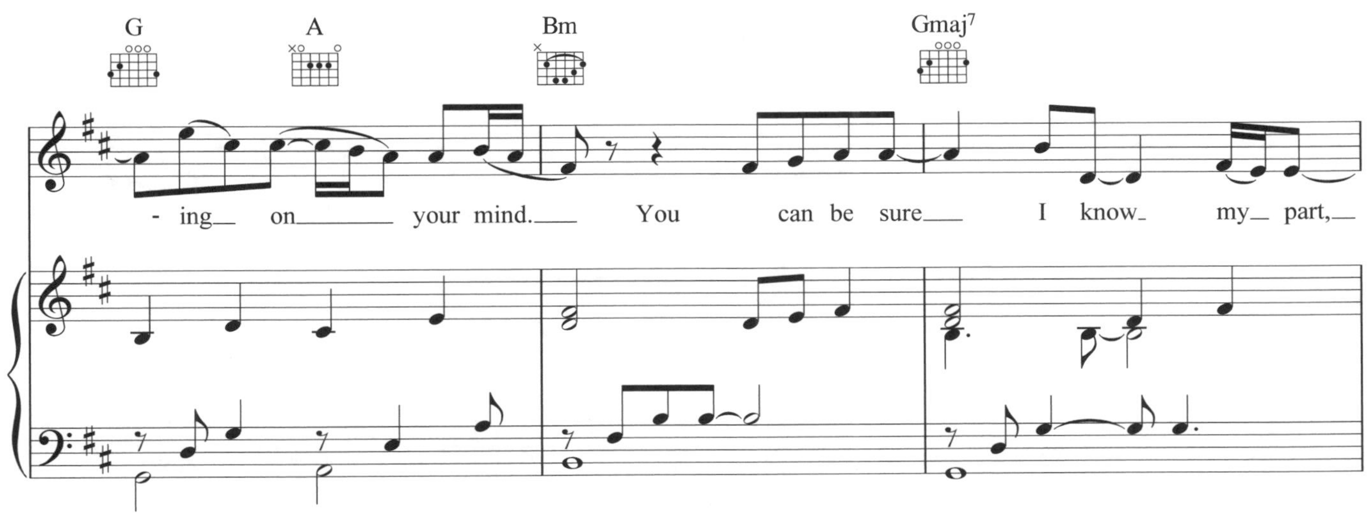
G
A
Bm
Gmaj7
- ing on your mind. You can be sure I know my part,

A
D
Bm7
A/C#
'cos I stand be- side you through the years,

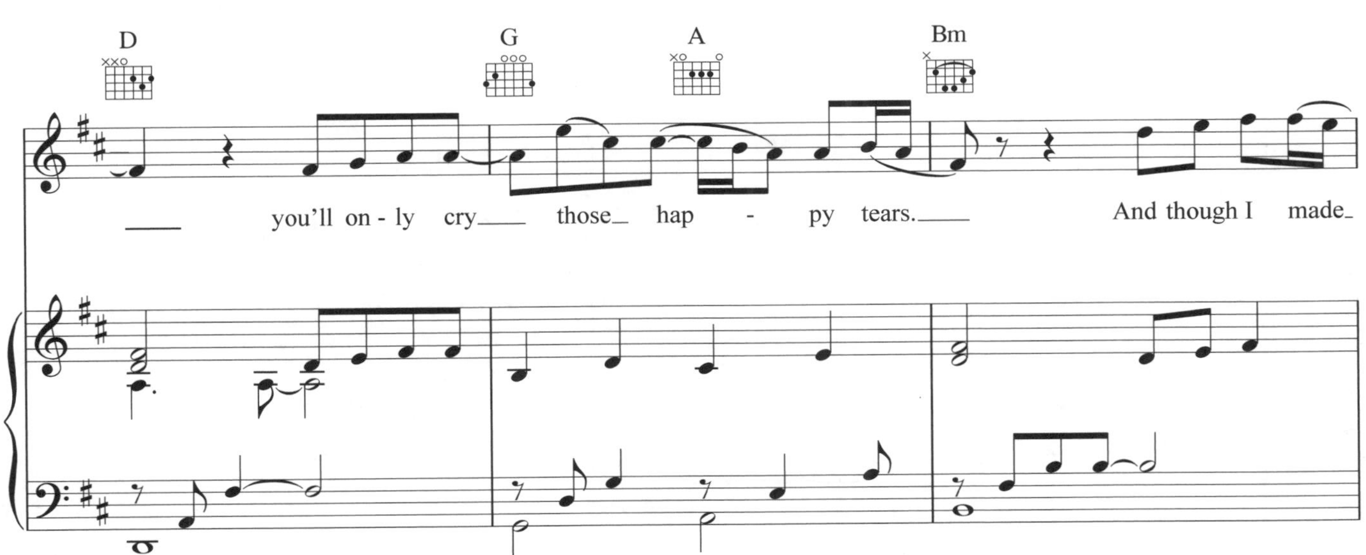
D
G
A
Bm
you'll on - ly cry those hap - py tears. And though I made

D/A
G♯7(♭5)
4fr
Asus4
A7
mis- take
I'll nev - er break your heart.
And I swear

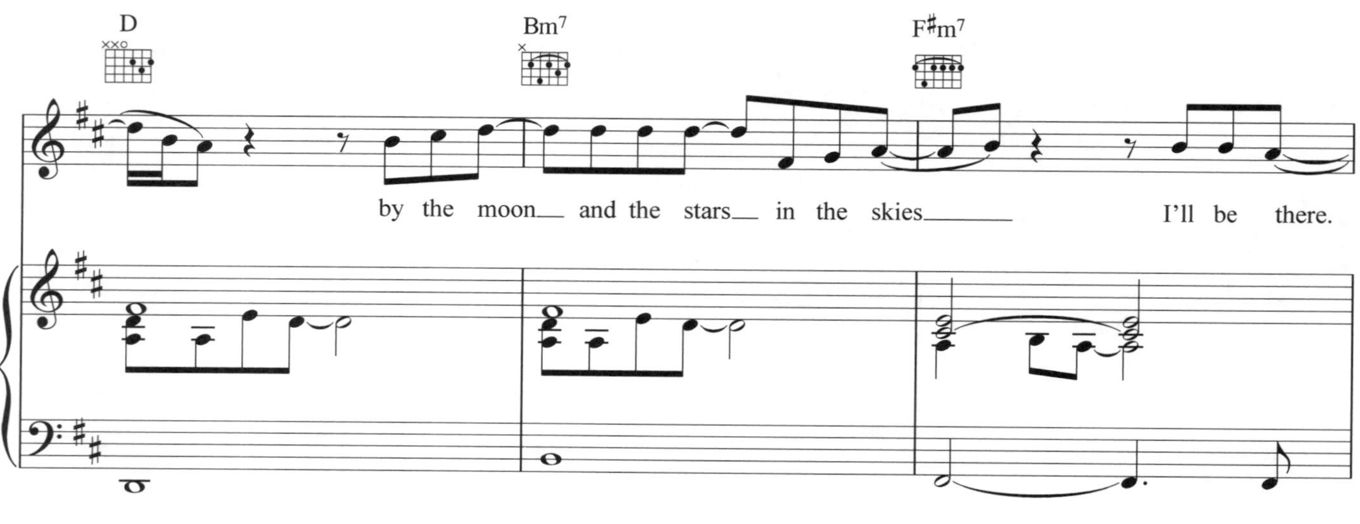
D
Bm7
F♯m7
by the moon and the stars in the skies
I'll be there.

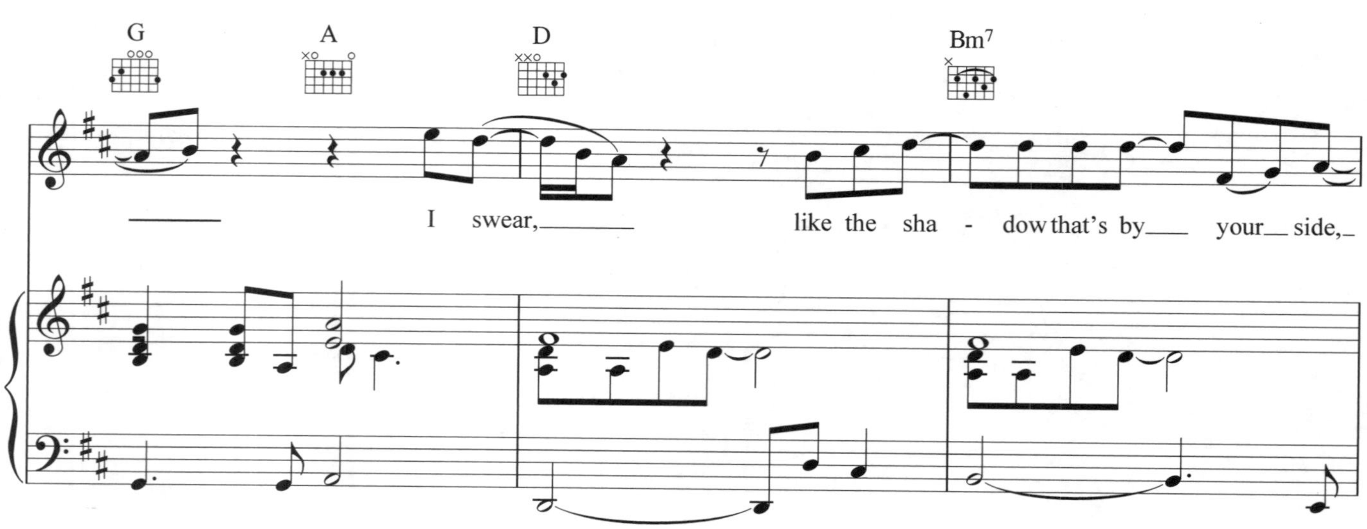
G
A
D
Bm7
I swear,
like the sha - dow that's by your side,

F♯m7
G
A
Em7
I'll be there for bet - ter or worse, 'til

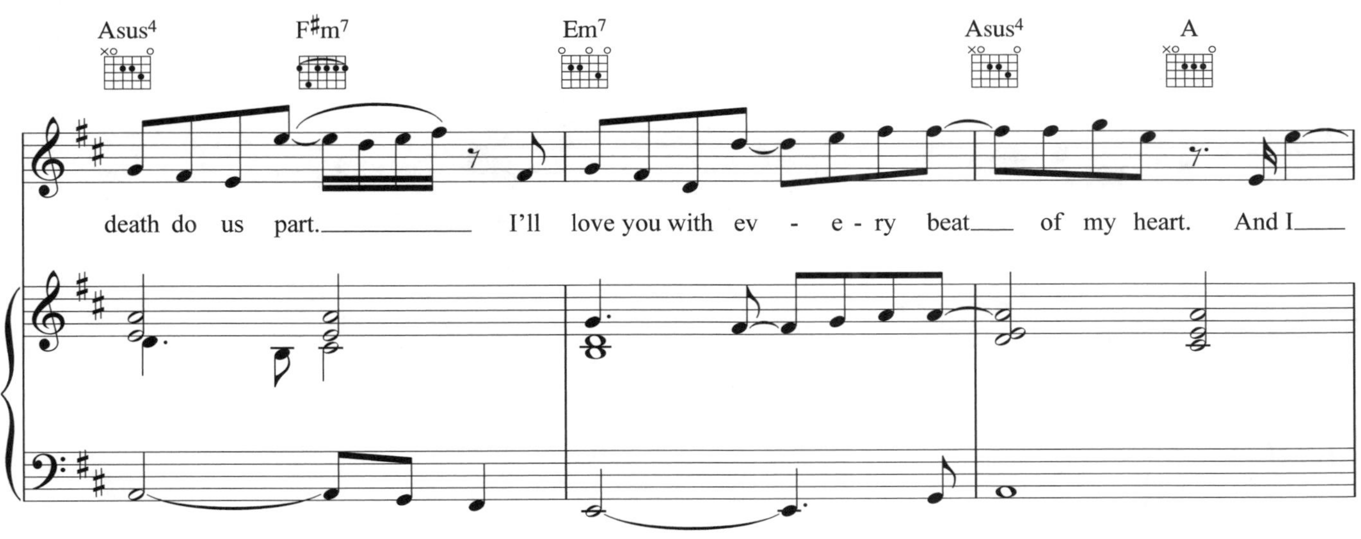
Asus4
F♯m7
Em7
Asus4
A
death do us part. I'll love you with ev - e - ry beat of my heart. And I

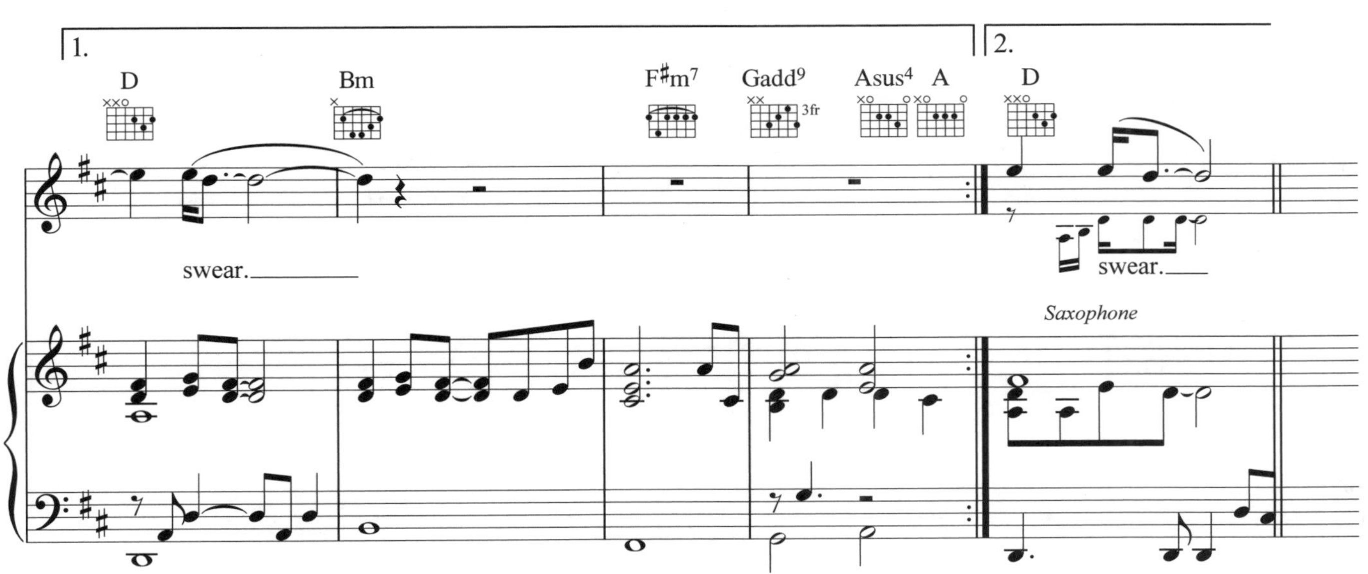
1.
2.
D
Bm
F♯m7
Gadd9
3fr
Asus4
A
D
swear.
swear.
Saxophone

Bm7
F♯m7
G
A
F♯m7
B7
I swear

E
C♯m7
4fr
Gmaj7
by the moon and the stars in the sky
I'll be there.

Amaj7
B7
E
C♯m7
4fr
I swear, like the sha - dow that's by your side,

Verse 2:

I'll give you everything I can
I'll build your dreams with these two hands
We'll hang some memories on the walls
And when just the two of us are there
You won't have to ask if I can still care
'Cos as the time turns the page
My love won't age at all.

And I swear *etc.*

I Want It That Way

Words & Music by Max Martin & Andreas Carlsson

F♯m D A F♯m D A
are two worlds a part, can't reach to your
(Verse 2 see block lyric)
F♯m D A F♯m E A
heart, when you say that I want it that way. Tell me
Dadd9 E F♯m Dadd9
why; ain't no - thin' but a heart - ache. Tell me why; ain't no - thin' but a
E F♯m Dadd9 E A
mis - take. Tell me why; I ne - ver wan - na hear you say

1.
2.
F♯m
E
A
C♯sus4
C♯
4fr
"I want it that - a way." Am I that a way."
F♯m
A/E
D
Now I can see that we've fal - len a - part from the way that it used to be,
Bm
E
F♯m
A/E
yeah. No mat - ter the dis - tance, I want you to know that
D
Esus4
E
Dmaj7
E
F♯m
deep down in- side of me, you are my fi - re, the one

Dmaj7
E
F#m
Dadd9
2fr
E
Amaj7
de - si - re. You are, you are, you are, you are.
F#m
E
Eadd9
F#
G#m
4fr
Don't wan - na hear you. Ain't no - thin' but a heart - ache.
Eadd9
F#
G#m
4fr
Eadd9
Ain't no - thin' but a mis - take. I ne - ver wan - na
F#
B
G#m
4fr
F#
B
hear you say "I want it that - a way." Tell me

Verse 2:
Am I your fire, your one desire?
Yes, I know it's too late, but I want it that way.

Tell me why *etc.*

If I Let You Go

Words & Music by Jorgen Elofsson, Per Magnusson & David Kreuger

Fsus4 F Dm Gm
I can't find the courage to show, to let-ting you know
Cm Fsus4 F E♭ F
I've nev-er felt so much love be-fore. And once a-gain I'm think-
D7(♭9) Gm Cm E♭ F
-ing a-bout tak-ing the ea-sy way out. But if I
C G/B Am7 G Fadd9
let you go I will nev-er know what my life would be hold-ing you close

Gsus4
G
Am
G
F add9
C/E
to me. Will I ev - er see you smil - ing back at me? Oh yeah.
Dm7
Dm7(♭5)
1.
C
How will I know if I let you go?
2.
C
Em7
F
If I let you go.
Gsus4
G
C
Em7
Ooh, ba - by.

F
Gsus4
G
F
G
Oh.
Once a - gain I'm think -
E7
Am
Dm
F
G
- ing a - bout
tak - ing the ea - sy way out.
N.C.
D
A/C♯
Bm7
A
But if I
let you go
I will
nev - er know
what my
Gadd9
fr3
Asus4
A
Bm
A
life would be
hold - ing you close
to me.
Will I
ev - er see
you smil-ing

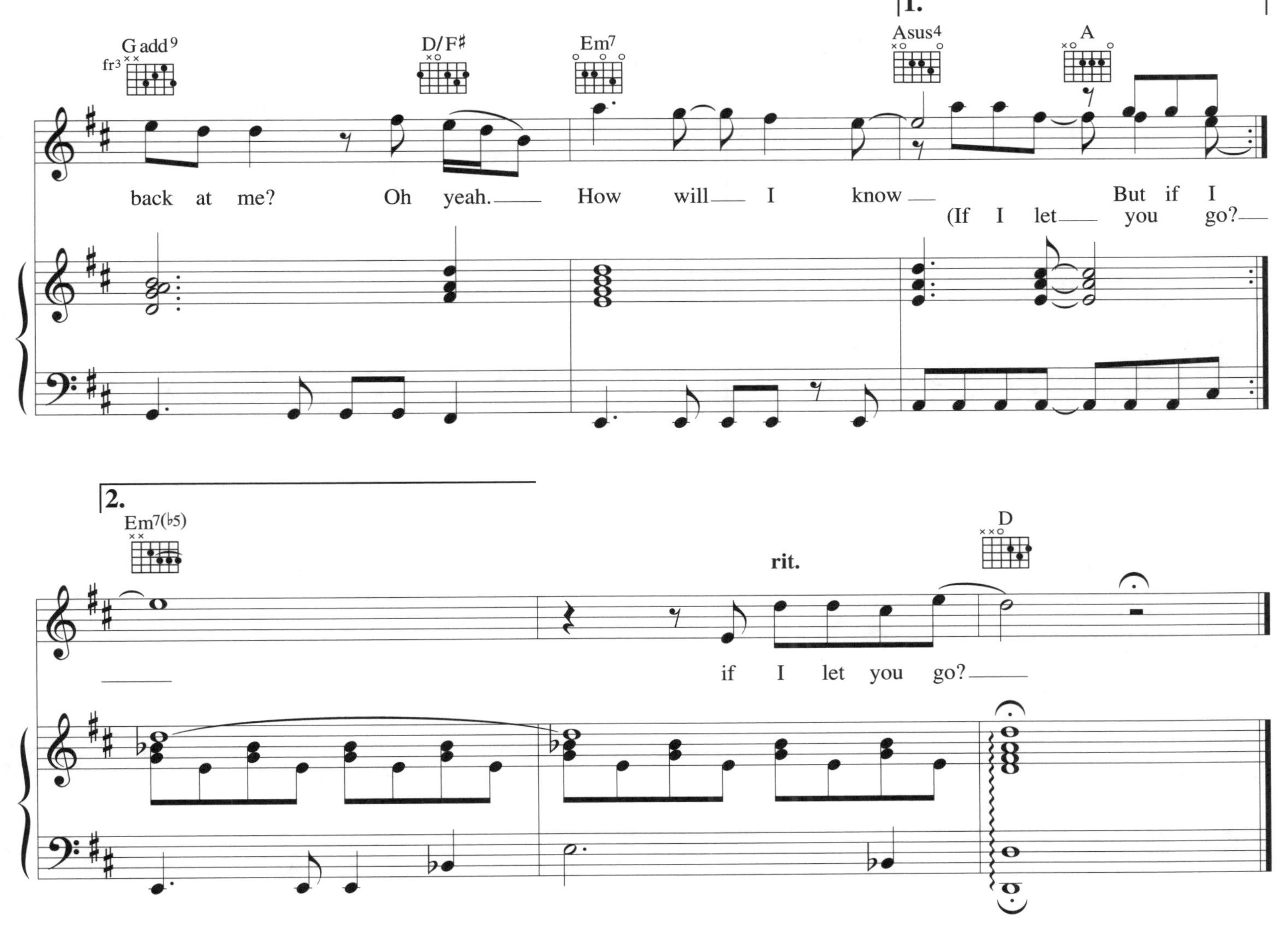

Verse 2:
Night after night I hear myself say
Why can't this feeling just fade away
There's no-one like you to speak to my heart
It's such a shame we're worlds apart
I'm too shy to ask, I'm too proud to lose
But sooner or later I've gotta choose
And once again I'm thinking about
Taking the easy way out.

But if I let you go *etc.*

If You Come Back

Words & Music by Ray Ruffin, Nicole Formescu, Ian Hope & Lee Brennan

B♭5
F/A
E♭5
6fr
F5
girl.
Oh, yes I have.
And
ev - er since the day you left me here a - lone,
I've been try -
G5
3fr
-in' to find
oh, the rea - son why.
So
B♭
E♭
F
if I did some - thin' wrong please tell me,
I wan - na un - der - stand.
'Cause

Gm
3fr
Gm9/F
3fr
E♭maj7
I don't want this love to ev - er end.
3
And I swear
B♭
B♭/D
E♭add9
3fr
F7
B♭
F/A
if you come back in my life
I'll be there till the end of time.
Oh,
E♭maj7
F11
B♭
B♭/D
E♭add9
3fr
F7
yeah.
And I swear
I'll keep you right by my side
'cause ba - by you're the
Gm7
3fr
F
1.
E♭maj7
F11
2.
E♭maj7
F11
one I want.
Oh,
yes you are.
3
yes you are.
3

Dm7
Gm
3fr
Dm7
May - be I did - n't know how to show it.
And may - be I did - n't know
Gm7
3fr
E♭maj7
what to say.
And this time I will hold this tight
Dm7
Cm7
3fr
F9sus4
then we can build our lives. So we can be as one. I swear
B♭
B♭/D
E♭add9
3fr
F7
if you come back in my life I'll be there till the

Verse 2:
I watched you go
Taking my heart with you
Oh, yes you did
Every time I try to reach you on the phone
Baby, you're never there
Girl, you're never home.

So if I did something wrong *etc.*

No Matter What

Music by Andrew Lloyd Webber
Lyrics by Jim Steinman

A
No mat - ter what they call us,
how - ev - er they at -
No mat - ter what they tell you,
no mat - ter what they
Bm/A
Bm
D/E
E
- tack,
no mat - ter where they take us,
do,
no mat - ter what they teach you,
Esus4
E
A
we'll find our own way back.
I can't de - ny what I
what you be - lieve is true.
And I will keep you safe
A7
D
be - lieve,
I can't be what I'm not.
and strong
and shel - tered from the storm.

Bm
D/E
E
Esus4
E7
I know our love's for - ev - er,
I know no mat - ter what.
No mat - ter where it's bar - ren
our dream is be - ing born.
1.
2.
A
A
C
Instrumental
Dm
Dm/G
G7
G
C

C
F/C
C
Dm
No mat-ter who they fol-low,
no mat-ter where they lead,
F/G
G7
Gsus4
G7
no mat-ter how they judge us
I'll be eve-ry one you need.
C
C7/E
No mat-ter if the sun don't shine,
F
C/E
Dm
or if the skies are blue.
No mat-ter what the

F/G G7 Gsus4 G7 C
end - ing, my life be - gan with you. I
C C7/E F rall. C/E
can't de - ny what I be - lieve, I can't be what I'm not.
Colla voce
Dm G7
I know this love's for ev - er, That's all that mat - ters now no mat - ter
a tempo
C2
Repeat to fade
No no mat - ter no. No no mat - ter no.
what. No no mat- - ter what. No no mat-

More Than Words

Words & Music by Nuno Bettencourt & Gary Cherone

B
C♯
D♯m
D♯m/A♯
G♯m
4fr
6fr
6fr
4fr
not to say, but if you on - ly knew how
C♯
F♯
C♯/E♯
D♯m
4fr
6fr
ea - sy it would be to show me how you feel,
G♯m
C♯
F♯7
4fr
4fr
more than words is all you have to do
B
Bm
F♯
to make it real. Then you would - n't have to say

D♯m
6fr
G♯m7
4fr
C♯
4fr
that you love me, 'cause I'd al - rea - dy
F♯
C♯/E♯
D♯m
6fr
know. What would you do if my heart
D♯m/A♯
6fr
B
G♯m7
4fr
was torn in two? more than words to show you feel,
C♯
4fr
F♯
that your love for me is real. What

C♯/E♯
D♯m
D♯m/A♯
B
would you say if I took those words a - way?
Then you could - n't make things new, just by say - ing I love you.
G♯m7
C♯
F♯
F♯/A♯
Badd9
G♯m
La di da, la di da, la di da da da, more than words.
F♯/A♯
Badd9
1.
G♯m7sus4
C♯
La di da, la di da.

2.
G♯m
4fr
Badd9
C♯
4fr
F♯
di di di da. More than words.
B
G♯m7
4fr
B
C♯
4fr
F♯
La di da la di da. Di di di da da, more than words.
Badd9
G♯m
4fr
Badd9
La da da, la di da, la
C♯
4fr
F♯
C♯/E♯
da da, more than words.

Verse 2:
Now I've tried to talk to you
And make you understand
All you have to do is close your eyes
And just reach out your hands
And touch me,
Hold me close don't ever let me go.
More than words
Is all I ever needed you to show
Then you wouldn't have to say
That you love me
'Cause I'd already know.

What would you do *etc.*

She Left Me

Words & Music by James Bourne & Thomas Fletcher

D
G
Bm
- more.
there.
Be - fore I could ask why, she was
And I've left mes - sa - ges af - ter the
Cadd9
Cm6
4fr
Bm7
gone out the door.
tone. (Real - ly?) Yeah man, loads.
And I did - n't know
I did - n't know
Em7
Bm7
Em7
what I did wrong.
what I did wrong.
But
But
C
Dsus4
D
N.C.
now I just can't move on.
now I just can't move on.
Since she

G
Bm
Cadd9
D
left me she told me, "Don't wor - ry, you'll be O. K. You don't
Bm
Em7
Cadd9
D
need me, be - lieve me, you'll be fine." Then I
To Coda
Em
Em/E♭
Em/D
Em/C♯
A9
knew what she meant and it's not what she said. Now
1.
Cadd9
Cm6
4fr
G
Bm
I can't be - lieve that she's gone.

2.
Cadd9
D
Cm6
4fr
Free time
N.C.
- lieve she's gone.
a tempo
G
Bm
Cadd9
D
G
Bm
Cadd9
Cm6
4fr
3
Bm
Em7
Bm

Em7
Cadd9
Dsus4
3
D
N.C.
D.S. al Coda
Well, since she
Coda
Cadd9
Free time
Cm6
4fr
N.C.
G
a tempo
I can't be - lieve that she's gone.
Bm
Cadd9
Cm6
4fr
rit.
Gmaj7
Yeah, yeah, yeah, yeah, yeah.

When The Lights Go Out

Words & Music by Eliot Kennedy, Tim Lever, Mike Percy, John McClaughlin, Sean Conlon, Jason Brown, Richard Dobson, Richard Breen & Scott Robinson

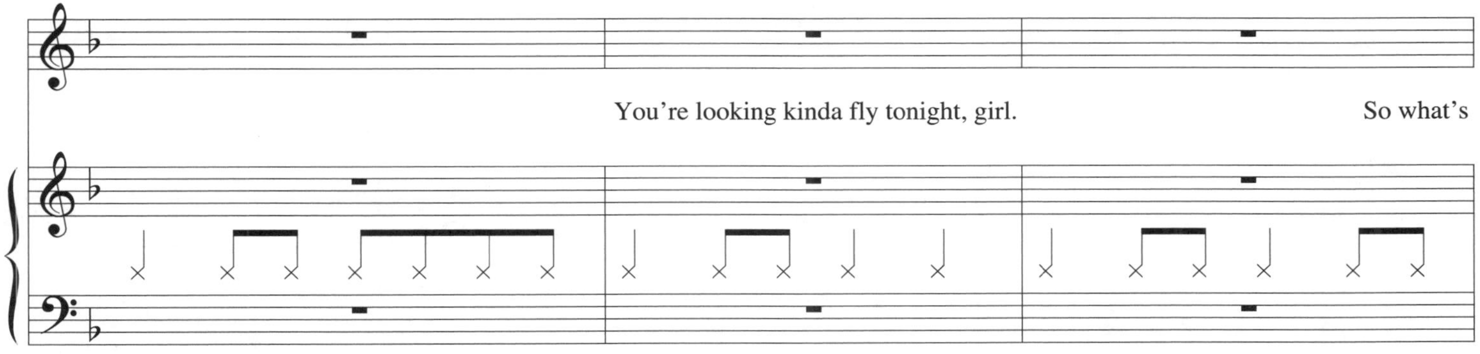

F
G7
B♭
A7
oh no, no, oh!
I'll show you what it's
Dm
A aug
F
G7
B♭
all a - bout.
(Spoken) Coming at you girl,
you know you like this girl.
C6
Dm
Here we go!
Check it.
Dm
A aug
F
G7
1. I ain't sor - ry for the way I feel,
I know you think I'm be - ing in - sin - cere,
(Verse 2 see block lyric)

B♭
A7
Dm
A aug
from the way I'm treat - ing you. I nev-er want-ed to be so un - kind,
F
G7
B♭
the on - ly one thing on my mind is just kick -
C6
B♭maj7
Cadd9
- ing it with you, girl. Ba - by, it's not the way I feel.
Gm9
fr3
B♭
You know you must be-lieve me now. Ba - by, it's not

Cadd9
N.C.
part of the deal, oh no, no. Ba - by, when the
Dm
A aug
F
G7
lights go out ev - 'ry sin - gle word could not ex -
B♭
A7
- press the love and ten - der - ness. I'll show you what it's
Dm
A aug
F
G7
all a - bout, babe I swear you will suc - cumb to

1.
B♭
C11
Dm
me, so ba - by come to me when the lights go out. (Spoken) Yeah
check it, check it out, second verse girl.
2, 3.
B♭
C11
me, so ba - by come to me. And ba - by when the
Dm
A aug
F/C
G7
lights go out ev - 'ry sin - gle word could not ex -
B♭
A7
Dm
A aug
- press the love and ten - der - ness. I'll show you what it's all a - bout, babe,

F
G7
B♭
C6
I swear you will suc-cumb to me, so ba-by, come to me when the lights go
Dm
out.
When I flick the switch, make your hips wan-na dip now. I can get you off cos I'm rea-dy and equip-ped now.
N.C.
Swing for me, ba-by, give me all that you got, nev-er wan-na stop cos ya make me feel hot.
I know what you wan - na do and that I feel the same way too.

Verse 2:
I know you think it may be just a lie
Ain't no good in putting up a fight
Cos my heart is set on you.
I see the truth is in your eyes
I ain't fooled by your thin disguise
I can see I'm getting through babe.
Girl, don't deny the way you feel
You know you gotta trust me
Give me the chance to prove I'm real, oh yeah, yeah.

Baby, when the lights *etc.*

You Raise Me Up

Words & Music by Rolf Lovland & Brendan Graham

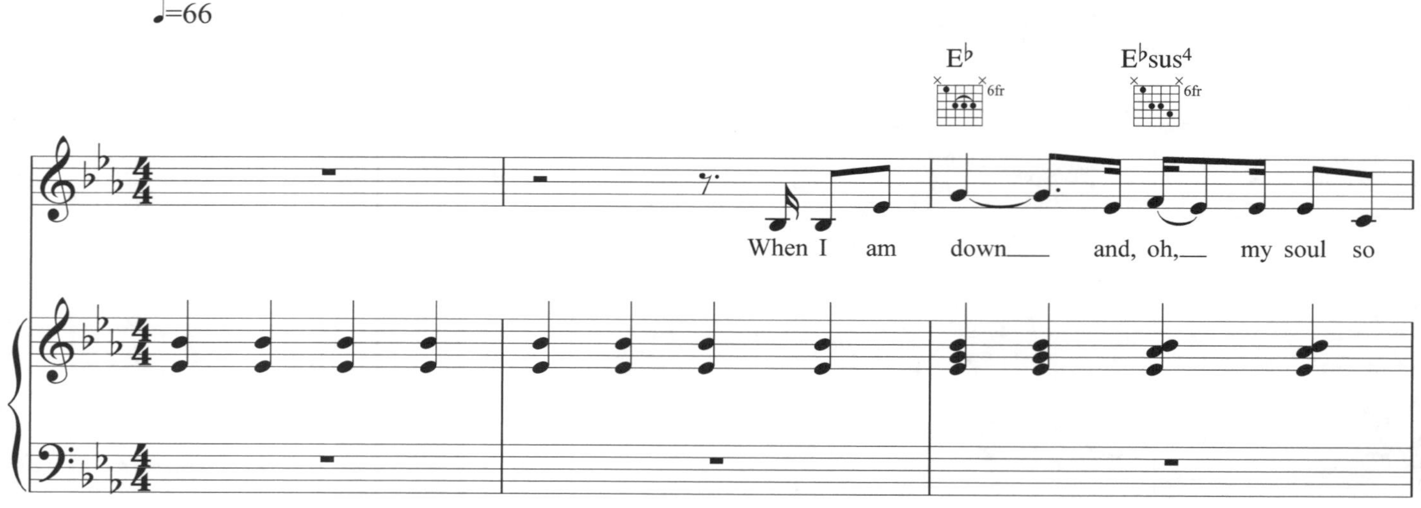

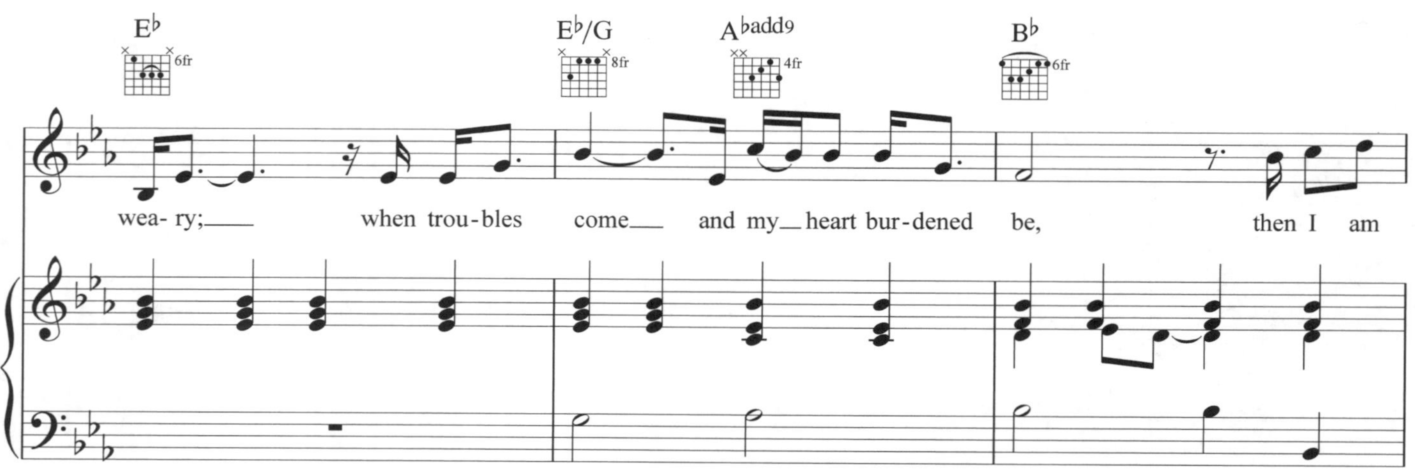

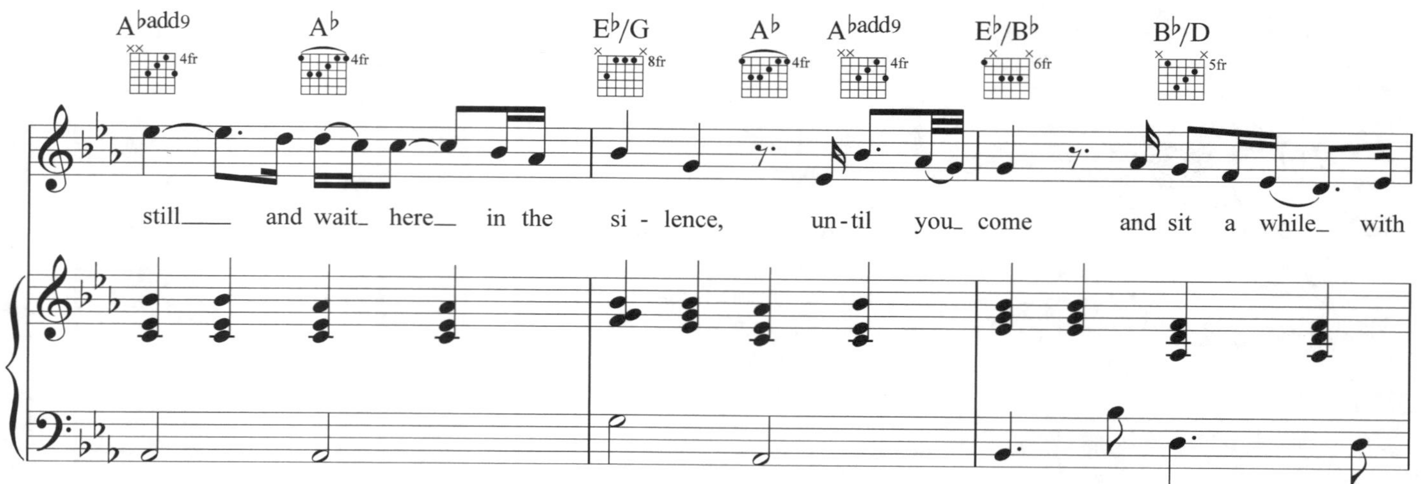

E♭
Cm
A♭
E♭/G
B♭/D
me. You raise me up so I can stand on moun - tains. You raise_ me
Cm
A♭
E♭/G
B♭
E♭
A♭
up to walk on storm - y seas. I am strong when I__ am on__ your
E♭/B♭
E♭/G
A♭
E♭/B♭
B♭sus4
B♭
E♭
shoul - ders.__ You raise_ me up to more_ than I__ can be.

F
Gm/F
3fr
F
F/C
F/A
B♭
F/C
Csus4
3fr
C
3fr
B♭/D
5fr
B♭
6fr
F/A
B♭
3
F/C
C
Csus7
F
Dm
B♭
You raise me up so I can stand on
F/A
C/E
Dm
Dm/C
B♭
F/A
poco rit.
C6
C
mountains. You raise me up to walk on storm-y seas. I am
3

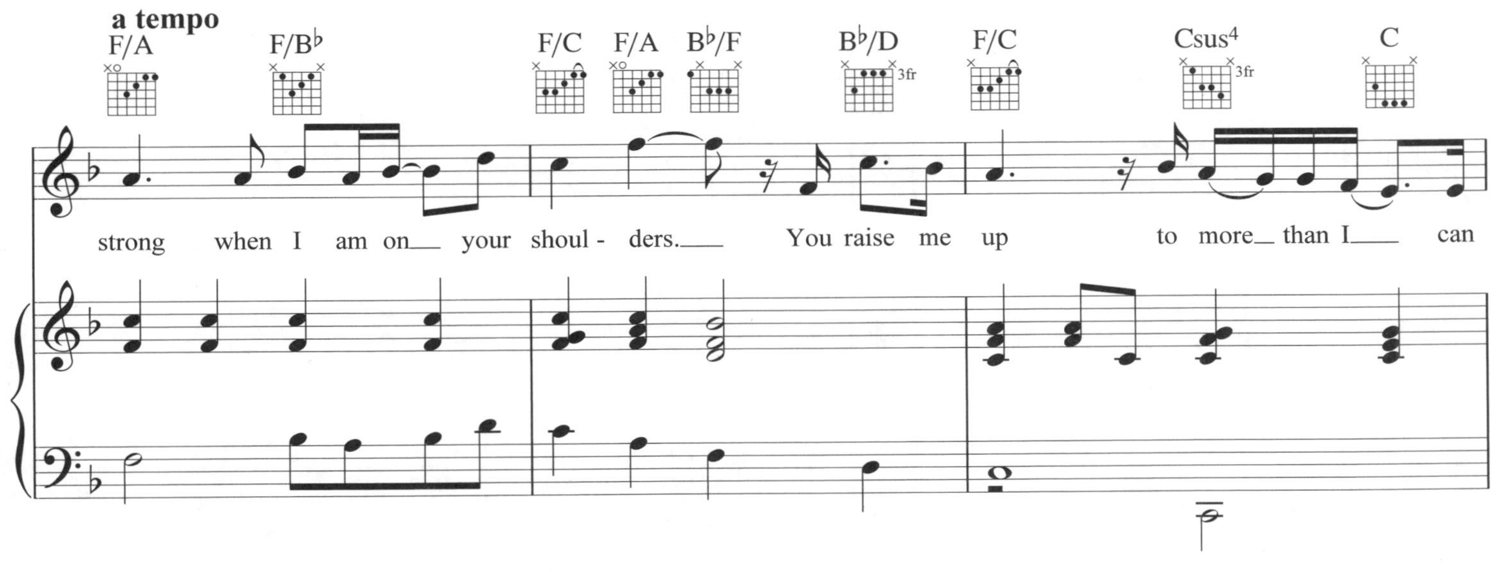
a tempo
F/A
F/B♭
F/C
F/A
B♭/F
B♭/D
3fr
F/C
Csus4
3fr
C
strong when I am on your shoul - ders. You raise me up to more than I can

rit.
F
B♭/F
F
a tempo
E♭m
6fr
C♭
7fr
be. You raise me up so I can stand on

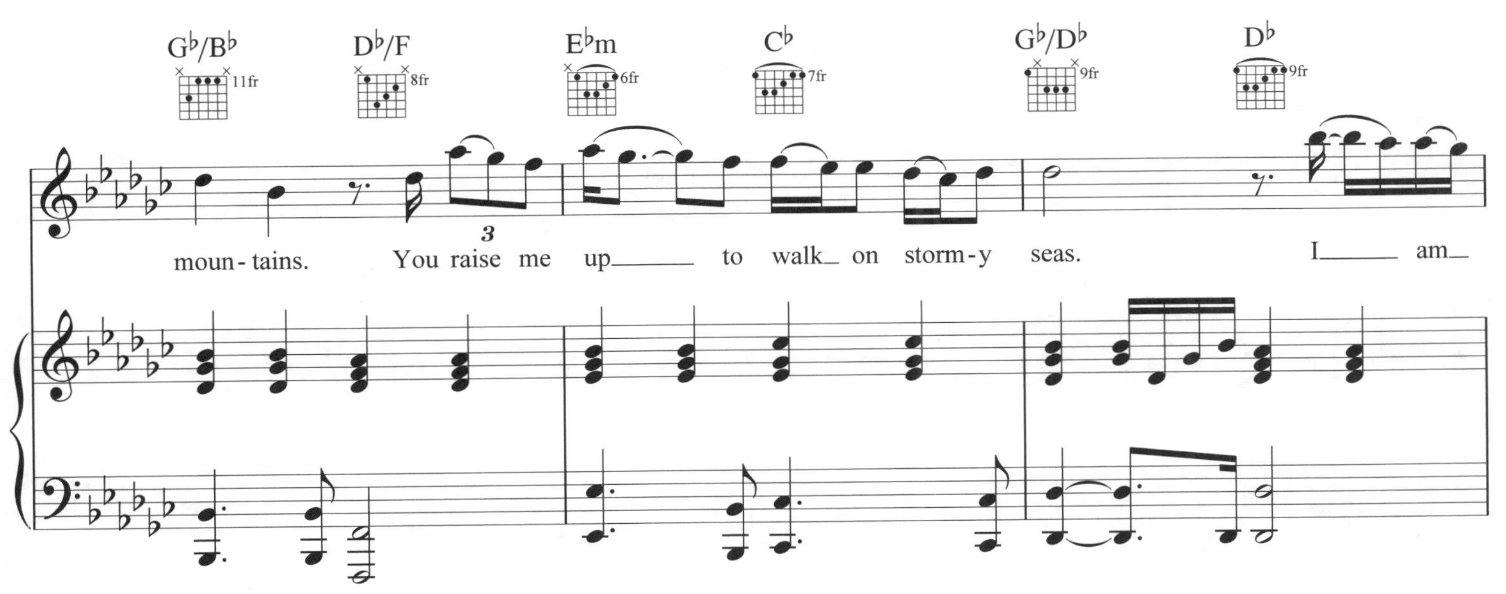
G♭/B♭
11fr
D♭/F
8fr
E♭m
6fr
C♭
7fr
G♭/D♭
9fr
D♭
9fr
3
moun - tains. You raise me up to walk on storm - y seas. I am

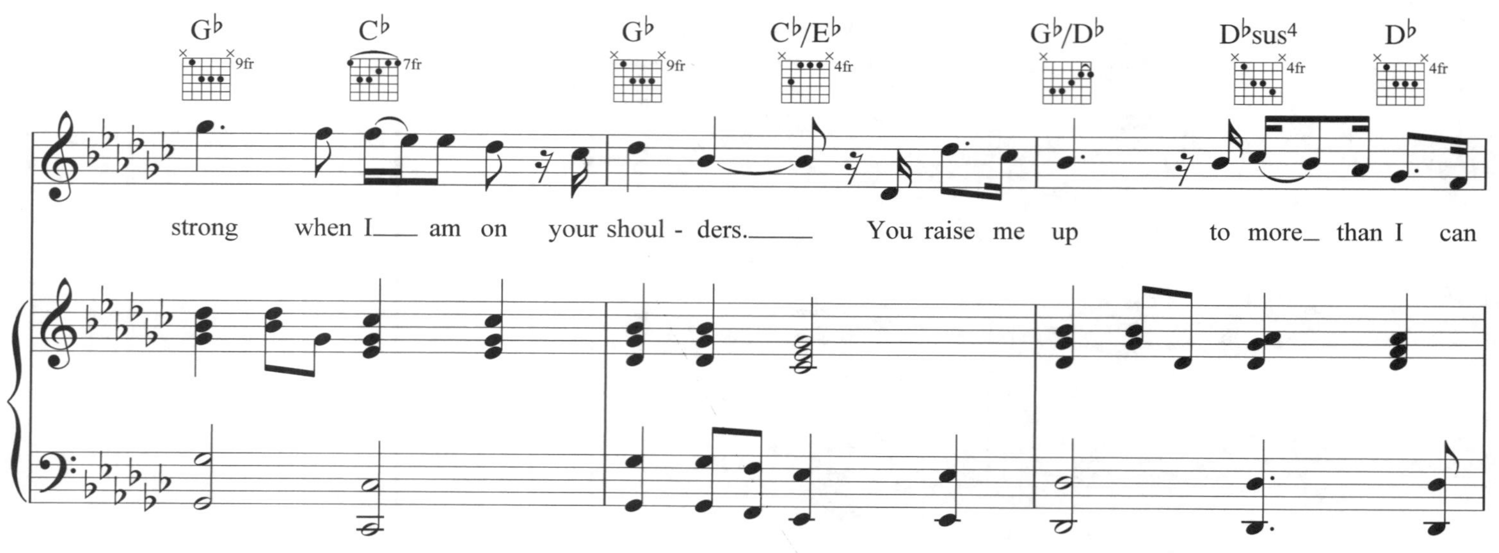
G♭
9fr
C♭
7fr
G♭
9fr
C♭/E♭
4fr
G♭/D♭
D♭sus4
4fr
D♭
4fr
strong when I am on your shoul - ders. You raise me up to more than I can

G♭
B♭7/D
5fr
E♭m
6fr
C♭
7fr
be. You raise me up so I can stand on

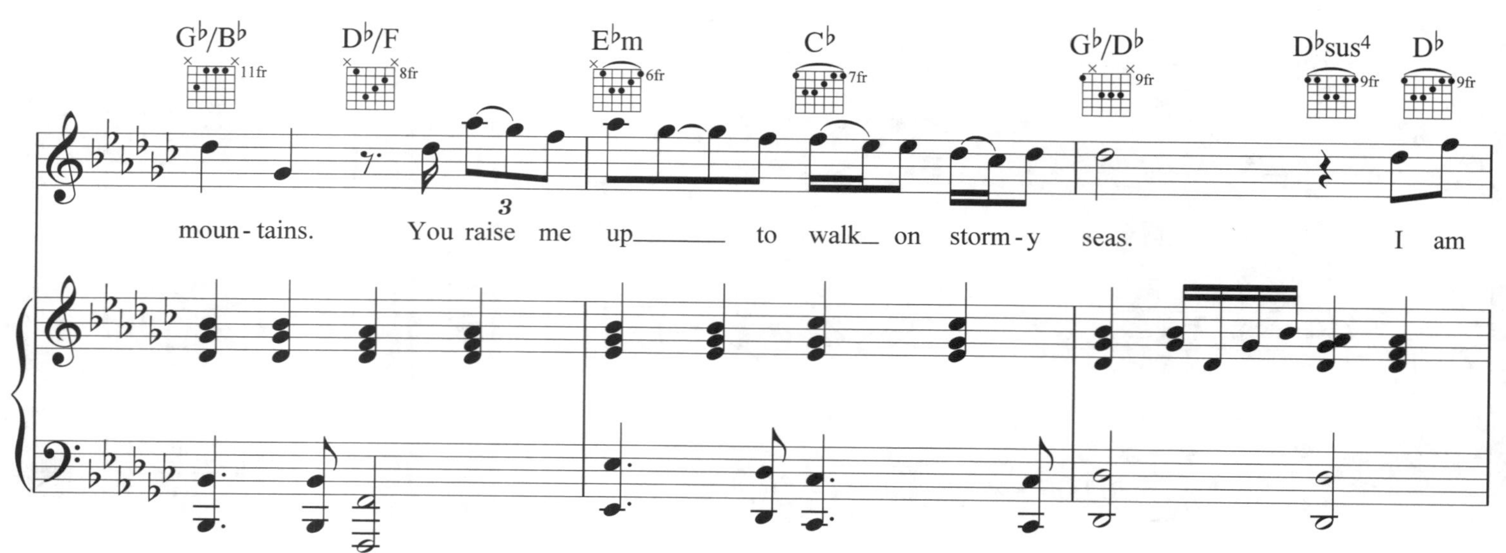
G♭/B♭
11fr
D♭/F
8fr
E♭m
6fr
C♭
7fr
G♭/D♭
9fr
D♭sus4
9fr
D♭
9fr
3
moun - tains. You raise me up to walk on storm - y seas. I am

G♭/B♭
C♭add9
G♭/D♭
G♭/B♭
C♭
G♭/D♭
D♭sus4
11fr
7fr
9fr
11fr
7fr
9fr
9fr
strong when I am on your shoul- ders. You raise me up to more than I can

poco rit.
meno mosso
E♭m
C♭add9
C♭
G♭/D♭
6fr
7fr
7fr
9fr
be. You raise me up to

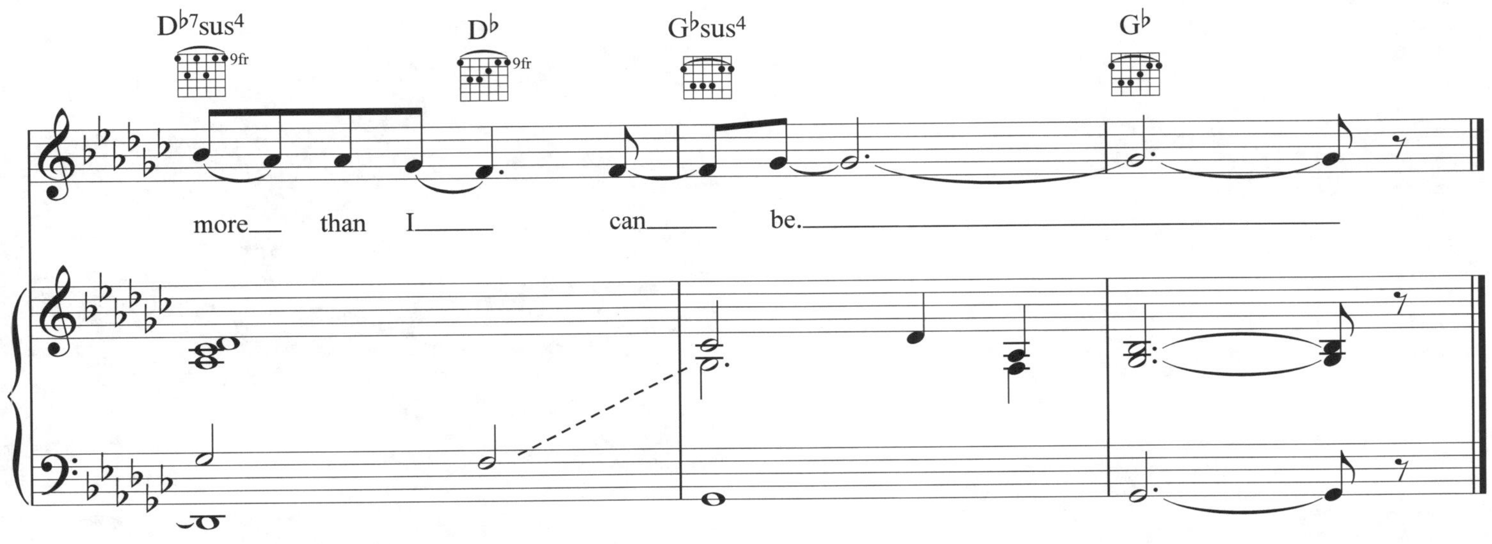
D♭7sus4
D♭
G♭sus4
G♭
9fr
9fr
more than I can be.

123456789

THE GREATEST BALLADS FROM THE BIGGEST BOY BAND ACTS!

14 SENSATIONAL SMASH HITS EXPERTLY ARRANGED FOR PIANO, VOICE & GUITAR TO MATCH THE SOUND OF THE ORIGINAL GROUP!

- ★ **McFLY** ALL ABOUT YOU
- ★ **BACKSTREET BOYS** ALL I HAVE TO GIVE
- ★ **BLUE** BEST IN ME
- ★ **BOYZONE** FATHER AND SON
- ★ **BLUE** GUILTY
- ★ **ALL-4-ONE** I SWEAR
- ★ **BACKSTREET BOYS** I WANT IT THAT WAY
- ★ **WESTLIFE** IF I LET YOU GO
- ★ **BLUE** IF YOU COME BACK
- ★ **BOYZONE** NO MATTER WHAT
- ★ **EXTREME** MORE THAN WORDS
- ★ **McFLY** SHE LEFT ME
- ★ **5IVE** WHEN THE LIGHTS GO OUT
- ★ **WESTLIFE** YOU RAISE ME UP

NOW YOU CAN PLAY AND SING YOUR OWN AUTHENTIC VERSION OF YOUR FAVOURITE BALLADS!

WISE PUBLICATIONS
part of The Music Sales Group
AM984907
www.musicsales.com

ISBN 1-84609-431-3
9 781846 094316
ISBN 13: 978-1-84609-431-6

Based on the best-selling keyboard method *by Kenneth Baker.*

THE COMPLETE KEYBOARD PLAYER

A superb compilation of popular songs arranged for all electronic keyboards. Includes suggested voices, fingering and lyrics, plus chord symbols and charts.

15 ALL-TIME FAVOURITES

JEAN